Clip-Art for
Science Teachers

Clip-Art for Science Teachers

ISBN 0-917623-30-4

Ventura Educational Systems
3440 Brokenhill Street
Newbury Park, CA 91320

Other Publications Include:

SuperGraph
GeoArt: Geometry and Art Discovery Unit
Marine Life: Anatomy of a Fish
                Anatomy of a Sea Lamprey
Plant and Animal Cells
The Plant: Nature's Food Factory
Chemaid: Introduction to the Periodic Table
The Worm: Invertebrate Anatomy
Protozoa: Introduction to Microorganisms
States: Geography Study Unit and Database
All About the Solar System
All About Simple Machines
Dr. Know: Experiments in Artificial Intelligence
Beginning Geometry

Coordinate Geometry
Geometry Concepts
Marine Invertebrates
Anatomy of a Shark
Algebra Concepts
VisiFrog: Vertebrate Anatomy
Senses: Human Physiology
Music Concepts
Computer Concepts
The Insect World
All About Matter
All About Light & Sound
Hands-On Math Series
Clip-Art for Math Teachers

Ventura Educational Systems
3440 Brokenhill Street
Newbury Park, CA 91320

(805) 499 - 1407
(800) 336 - 1022

Clip-Art for
Science Teachers

A collection of drawings and diagrams for creating
science related instructional materials.

Artwork drawn by:
Fred Ventura, Ph.D.

Copyright Notice

This product is intended for use by individuals and schools. The purchaser is entitled to use this product but <u>not</u> to transfer or sell reproductions of the software product or manual to other parties.

The software and manual are copyrighted by Ventura Educational Systems. All rights and privileges guaranteed by the copyright laws of the United States are reserved.

Disclaimer of Warranty and Limited Warranty

The software and accompanying written materials are provided "as is" without warranty of any kind. Ventura Educational Systems does not warrant, guarantee, or make any representations regarding the use, or the results of the use of the software or written materials in terms of correctness, accuracy, reliability, or currentness, or otherwise. The entire risk as to the results and performance of the software is assumed by the user.

The software is provided on a 3.5" floppy diskette for use on a single Macintosh™ computer. Ventura Educational Systems warrants that the media on which the software is recorded is free from defects in materials and workmanship under normal use and service for a period of thirty (30) days. Ventura Educational Systems' entire liability and exclusive remedy to the purchaser is to either refund the purchase price if the software is returned, or to replace the disk that does not meet the Ventura Educational Systems limited warranty.

The above are the only warranties of any kind, either express or implied, including but not limited to the implied warranties of merchantability and fitness for a particular purpose, that are made by Ventura Educational Systems on the product. No oral or written information or advice given by Ventura Educational Systems or its dealers, distributors or agents or employees shall create a warranty or in any way increase the scope of this warranty, and you may not rely on any such information or advice. This warranty gives you specific legal rights. You may have other rights which vary from state to state.

Neither Ventura Educational Systems nor anyone else associated with the development of this product shall be liable for any direct, indirect or consequential, or incidental damages arising out of the use of or inability to use this product.

Legitimate Usage of Clip-Art

As a legitimate owner of Clip-Art for Science Teachers you are entitled to keep a backup copy of the disk. The disk is not copy-protected. Use the Finder to transfer the files on the original disk to another disk. Instructions on how to make a copy can be found in the Macintosh owner's manual.

Please do not give or trade copies of this product to others. Only the original purchaser is entitled to use the product. Giving or trading copies of the clip-art drawings is not permitted.

Printed material that contains reproductions of the clip-art drawings may be reproduced for educational purposes only and may not be sold or used in material which is to be sold.

Programs that Work with Clip-Art for Science Teachers

There are many graphics, publishing and word processing programs which can be used with Clip-Art for Science Teachers. The images provided in this clip-art product are in MacPaint file format. Most of the commercially available programs that are used for page layout and desktop publishing accept bit-mapped MacPaint images.

 Clip-art for Science Teachers images are stored as "paint" documents. The resolution of an image is 72 dpi (dots per inch). A better quality image will result when the output is produced on an Apple LaserWriter if the image is reduced. The resolution of a LaserWriter is 300 dpi.

Some of the programs which can be used with Clip-Art for Science Teachers are listed. Other programs may also be used.

CricketPaint ....**Cricket Software**
CricketDraw ....**Cricket Software**
DeskPaint.......................**Zedcor, Inc.**
FullWrite.........................**Ashton-Tate, Inc.**
MacPaint........................**Apple Computer, Inc.**
FullPaint.........................**Ashton Tate, Inc.**
SuperPaint......................**Silicon Beach Software, Inc.**
Microsoft Word..............**Microsoft, Inc.**

Folders

The Clip-Art files are organized into six folders. Each of the folders contains a variety of files.

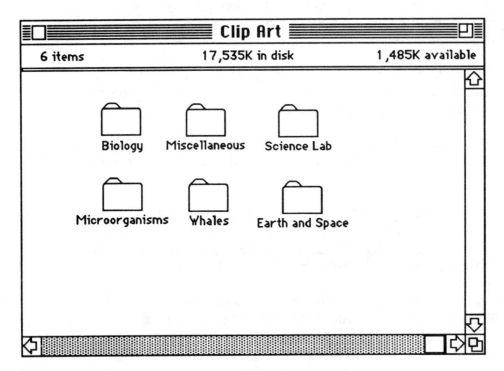

Paint and Clip-Art for Science Teachers

FullPaint   DeskPaint™   Cricket Paint 1.0

MacPaint when it was first introduced set a standard for graphics software. Since the release of MacPaint other programs have been developed which operate in a similar manner. Customarily these programs are collectively called Paint programs. Paint programs generally are used to produce what is called a bit-mapped image. Bit-mapped images are made up of tiny dots called pixels. The standard resolution for this type of image is 72 dots per inch or dpi. In order to move one of the images provided with Clip-Art for Science Teachers to a new project the image should first be stored in the clipboard.

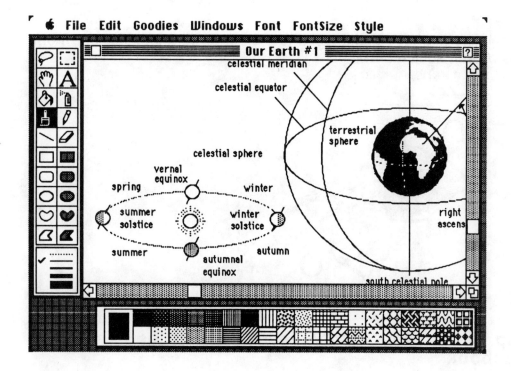

Paint programs generally have two tools for moving an image or portion of an image to the special memory area called the clipboard. The lasso and marquee are use to mark an object or section of a drawing and move the image to the clipboard.

The lasso tool is used to extract a <u>free-form</u> shape from the clip-art source drawing.

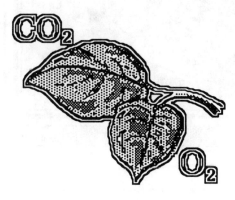

The marquee tool is used to extract a <u>rectangular</u> shape from the clip-art source drawing.

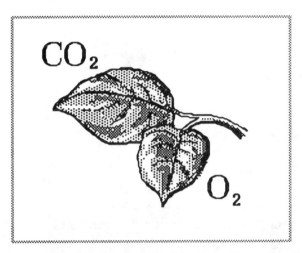

Using Clip-Art for Science Teachers with the Scrapbook

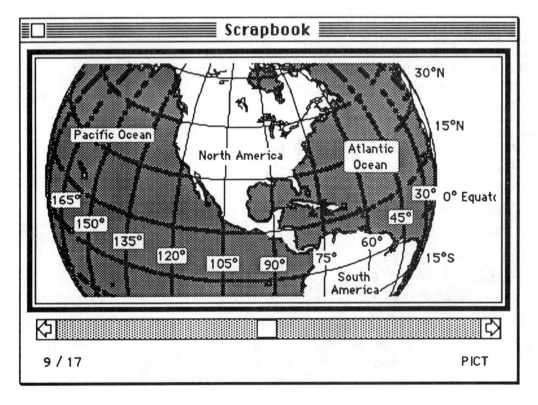

The Scrapbook is a great concept and helps to make the Macintosh an extremely versatile computer. The Scrapbook is a desk accessory and is used to store text, graphics, and other types of data so that the data can be freely passed from one type of information to another.

Users of clip-art may find that it is useful to place the images from the clip-art source files in the scrapbook so that the images can be quickly accessed when using word processing and page-layout programs.

Tip: The Macintosh system automatically uses the scrapbook file that is in the system folder of the start-up disk and that has the name Scrapbook File. Other scrapbook files can be stored on the start-up disk if a different name is used. For example to use the scrapbook file with the name "Biology Scrapbook" first change the name of the "Scrapbook File" to something else, then change the name of the "Biology Scrapbook" to "Scrapbook File".

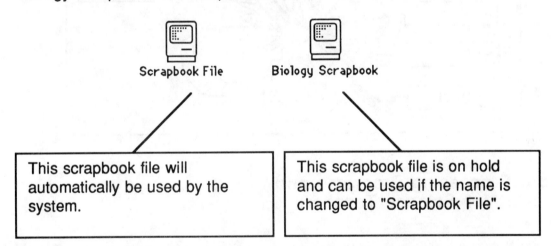

Draw Programs and Clip-Art for Science Teachers

Like MacPaint, MacDraw also set a standard when it was first introduced. Several programs have been developed that work in a similar way to MacDraw. Cricket Draw and DeskDraw are two such programs. Instead of using the bit-mapped technique that is used in "paint" programs, "draw" programs are object oriented graphics programs. The drawing is produced by creating a series of geometric objects. Draw programs can also accept bit-mapped graphics images, but generally do not allow the user to edit the bit-mapped images. Note: Some programs such as SuperPaint can switch between the paint mode and the draw mode.

Bit-mapped objects can be moved from the clipboard or the scrapbook into a draw-type of program and can be enhanced with labels and lines.

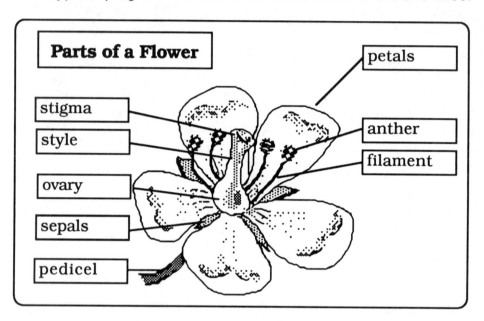

Word Processing Programs and Clip-Art for Science Teachers

Most Macintosh word processing programs allow for graphics to be incorporated into the text. The graphic images can be imported into the word processing document through the cut and paste technique. Graphic images stored in the scrapbook can be easily pasted into documents created with Microscoft Word or Microsoft Works.

Instructional materials such as the sample worksheet on the digestive system of a frog can be created with Clip-Art for Science Teachers and a word processing program.

Name:_____Date:_____

Anatomy of a Frog: Digestive System

Label the stomach, pancreas, intestine, and cloaca (anus).

The frog's alimentary canal begins at the mouth (buccal cavity) and terminates at the cloaca. The alimentary canal and the related organs and glands make up the digestive system. Frog's are primarily carnivorous and survive by eating insects, spiders, worms and other small creatures found in their environment. The frog does have tiny teeth but they are not used for chewing and food is swallowed whole.

Write a complete sentence to answer each of these questions.

1. How do frogs catch their prey?

   _____
   _____
   _____

2. What is the role of the stomach in the digestive process?

   _____
   _____
   _____

Directory of Clip-Art Images

Biology
Anatomy of a Clam #1
Anatomy of a Clam #2
Anatomy of a Frog #1
Anatomy of a Frog #2
Anatomy of a Frog #3
Anatomy of a Frog #4
Anatomy of a Frog #5
Anatomy of a Worm #1
Anatomy of a Worm #2
Marine Life #1
Marine Life #2
Parts of Plants
Sense Organs #1
Sense Organs #2

Earth and Space
Crystals
Our Earth #1
Our Earth #2
Our Earth #3
Our Earth #4
Our Earth #5
Solar System #1
Solar System #2

Microorganisms
Protozoa #1
Protozoa #2

Miscellaneous
Dinosaurs
Odds and Ends
Science Bits
U.S. Maps

Science Lab
Chemistry
In the Lab
Microscopes and Telescopes
Scientists #1
Scientists #2

Whales
Whales #1
Whales #2
Whales #3

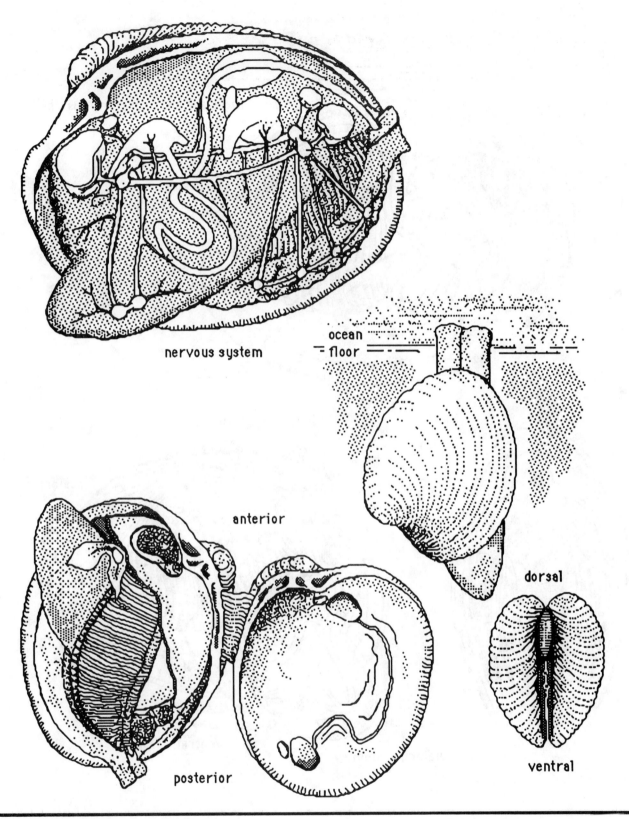

nervous system

ocean
floor

anterior

dorsal

posterior

ventral

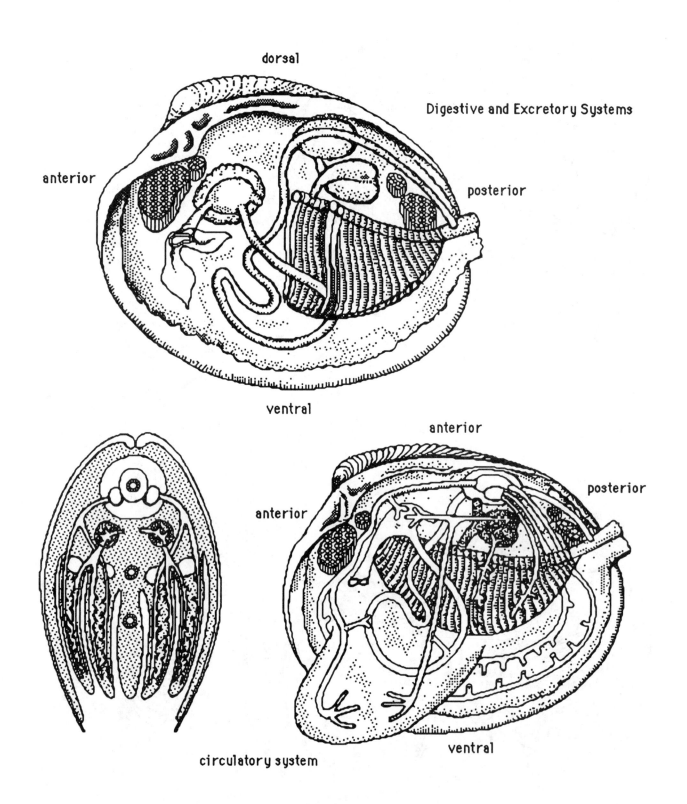

dorsal

Digestive and Excretory Systems

anterior

posterior

ventral

anterior

anterior

posterior

circulatory system

ventral

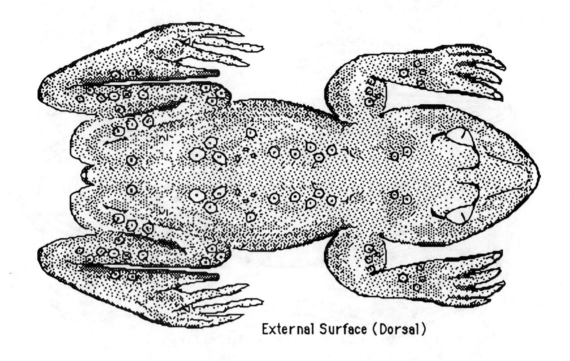

External Surface (Dorsal)

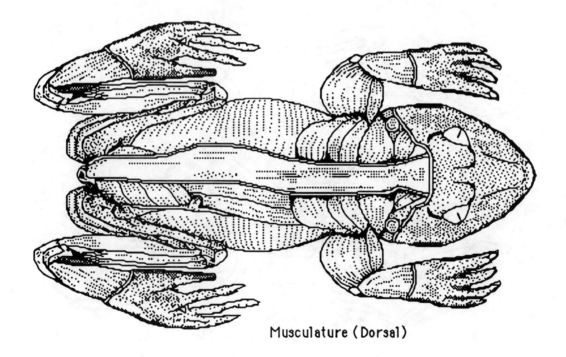

Musculature (Dorsal)

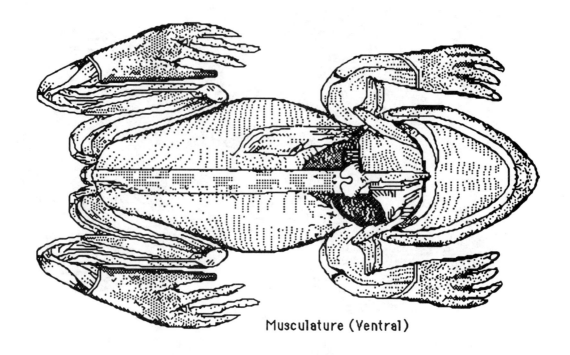

Musculature (Ventral)

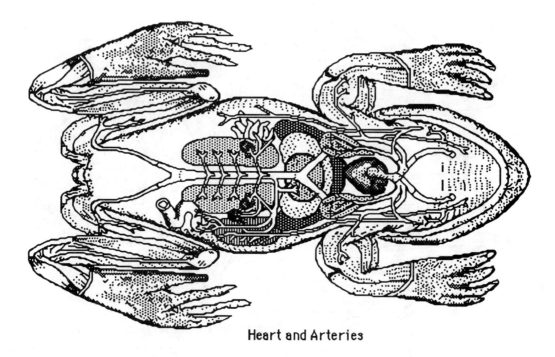

Heart and Arteries

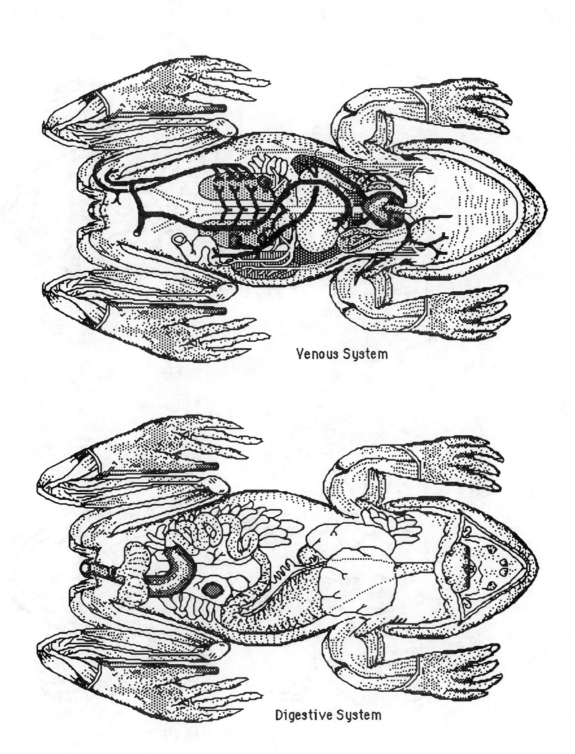

Venous System

Digestive System

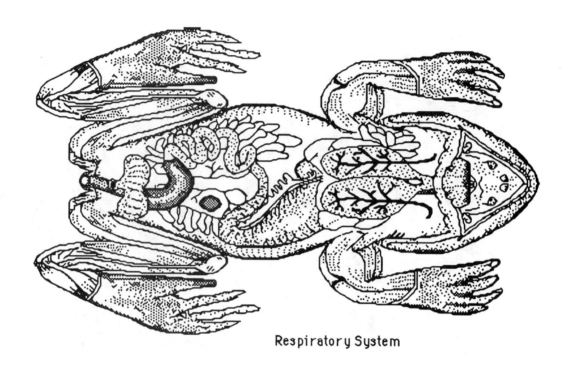

Respiratory System

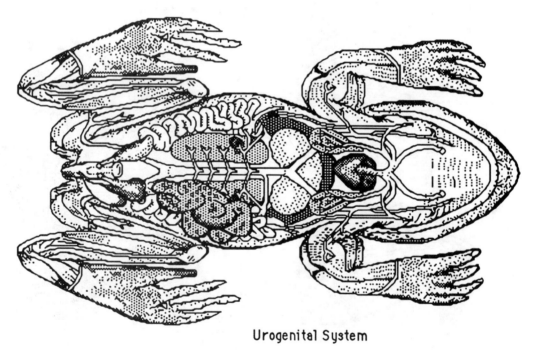

Urogenital System

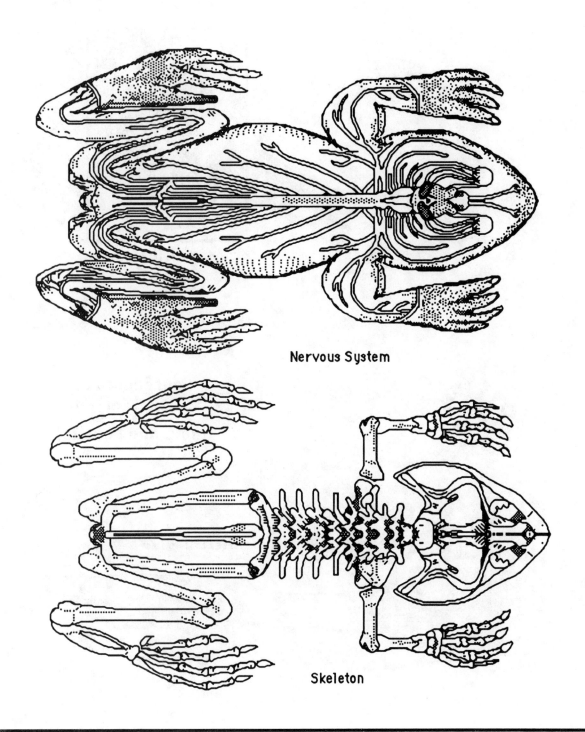

Nervous System

Skeleton

Digestive System

Surface Close-up

Posterior

Anterior

Magnification

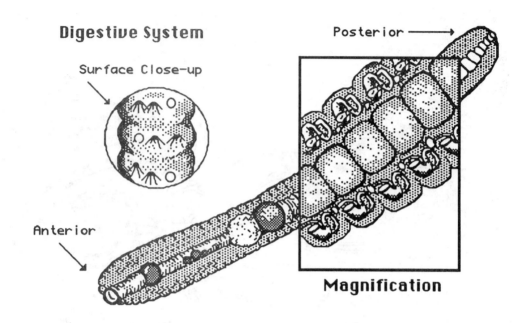

Reproductive System
(Male and Female)

Internal View

head

COPULATION

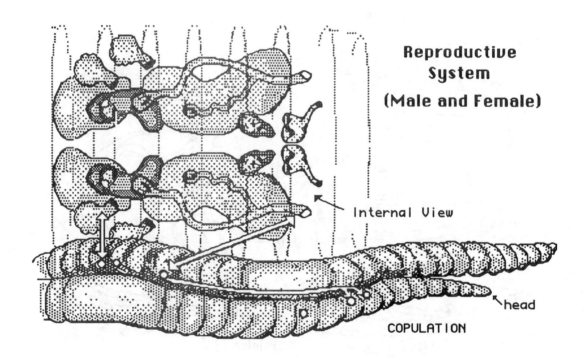

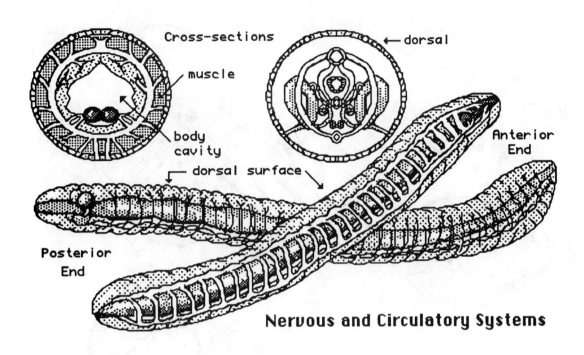

Cross-sections

muscle

body cavity

dorsal surface

←— dorsal

Anterior End

Posterior End

Nervous and Circulatory Systems

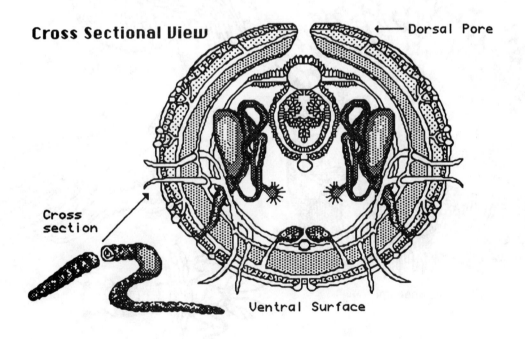

Cross Sectional View

←— Dorsal Pore

Cross section

Ventral Surface

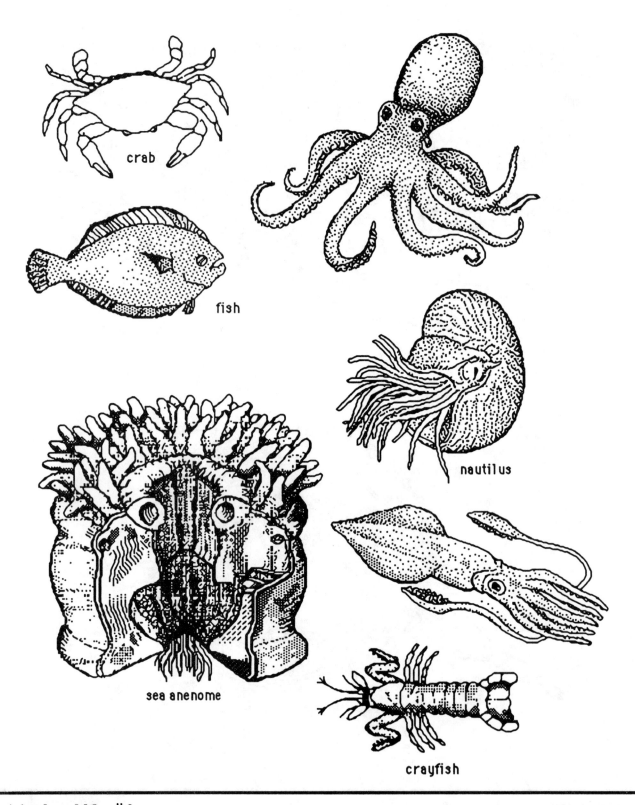

crab

fish

octopus

nautilus

sea anenome

crayfish

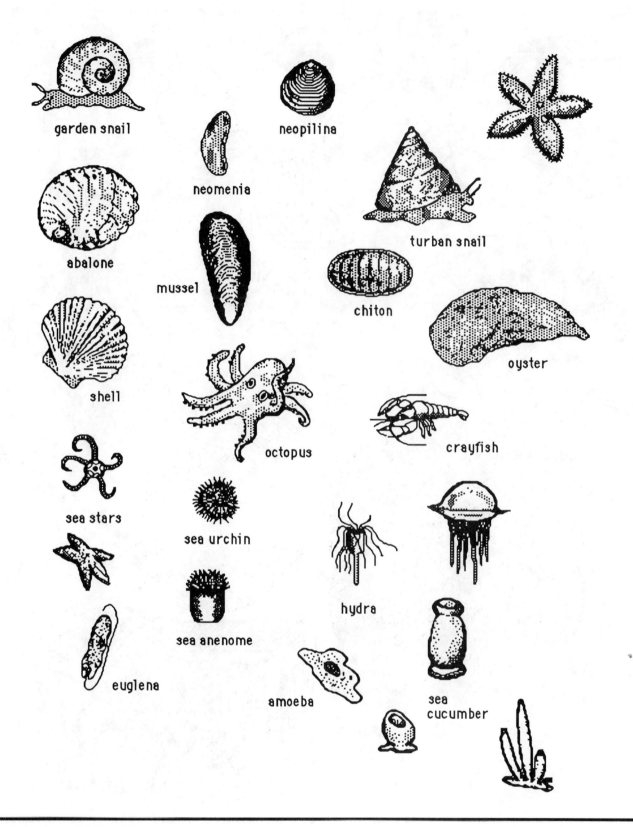

garden snail

neopilina

neomenia

abalone

mussel

turban snail

chiton

shell

oyster

octopus

crayfish

sea stars

sea urchin

hydra

sea anenome

amoeba

sea
cucumber

euglena

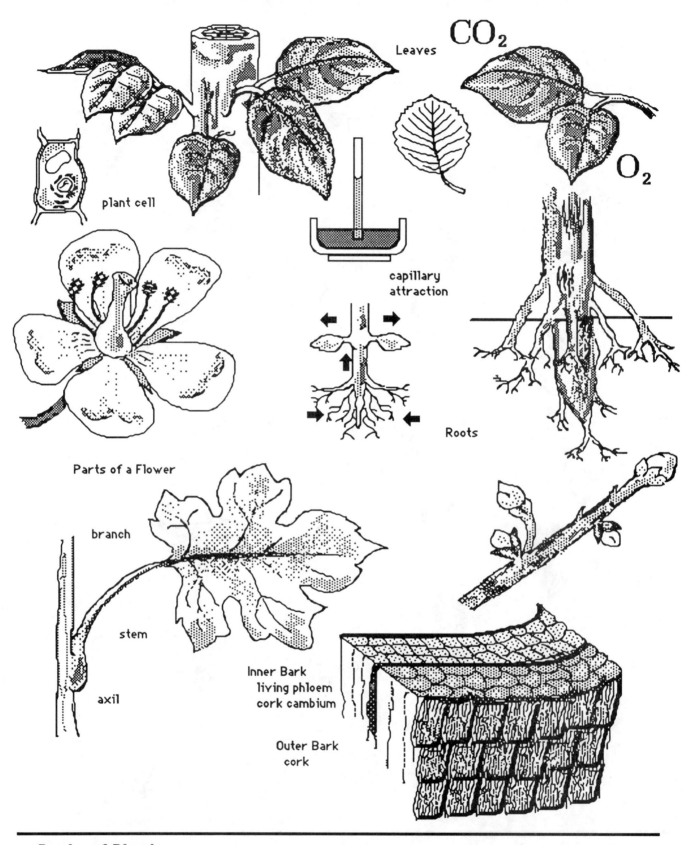

Leaves

CO$_2$

plant cell

O$_2$

capillary attraction

Roots

Parts of a Flower

branch

stem

axil

Inner Bark
living phloem
cork cambium

Outer Bark
cork

Parts of Plants

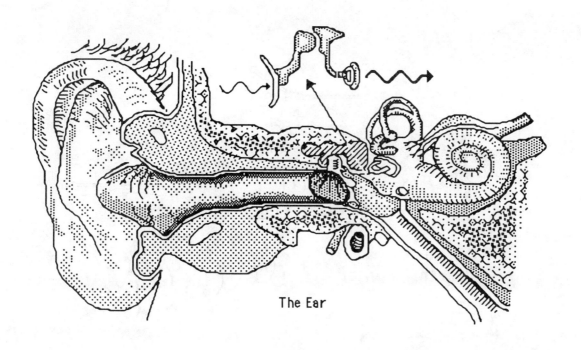

The Ear

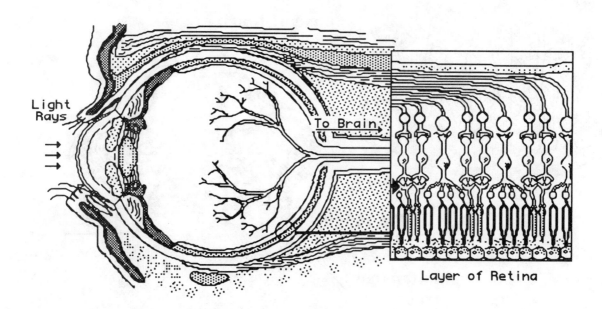

Light Rays

To Brain

Layer of Retina

The Eye

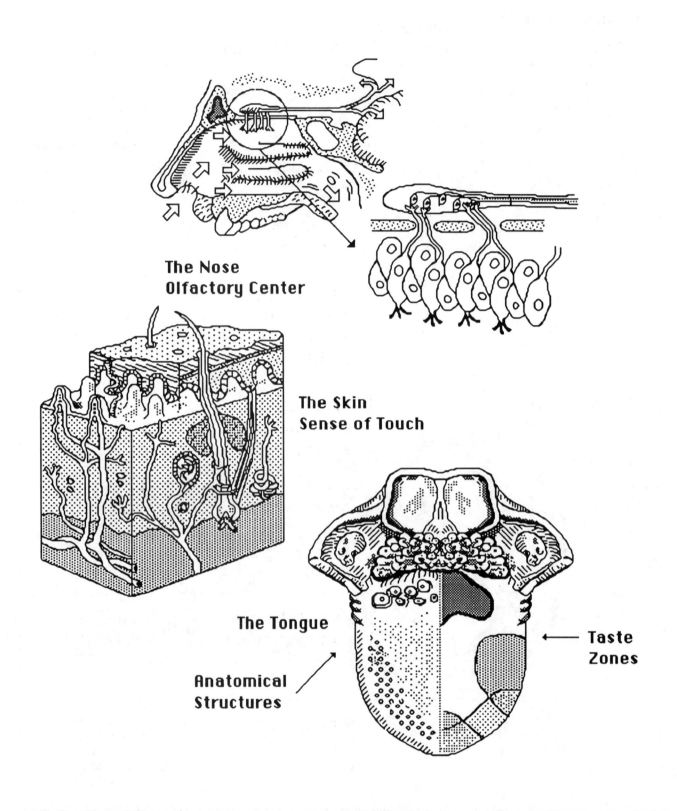

The Nose
Olfactory Center

The Skin
Sense of Touch

The Tongue

Anatomical
Structures

Taste
Zones

Shapes of Crystals

Type	Number of Surfaces	Shape of Surfaces	Examples
cubic	6	All are square	alum, pyrite silver, gold diamond, garnet sodium chloride
tetragonal	6	4 rectangles 2 squares right angles	zircon, white tin
orthorhombic	6	All rectangles 3 pairs of rectangles with different sizes right angles	topaz, rhombic sulfur, Epsom salt,
rhombohedral	6	rhombuses on all sides, no right angles	calcite
monoclinic	6	4 rectangles 2 parallelograms 16 right angles 8 other angles	gypsum, sugar borax
triclinic	6	parallelograms no right angles	boric acid, copper sulfate
hexagonal	8	2 hexagons 6 rectangles right angles	ice, ruby, apatite, emerald, quartz, sapphire

Crystals

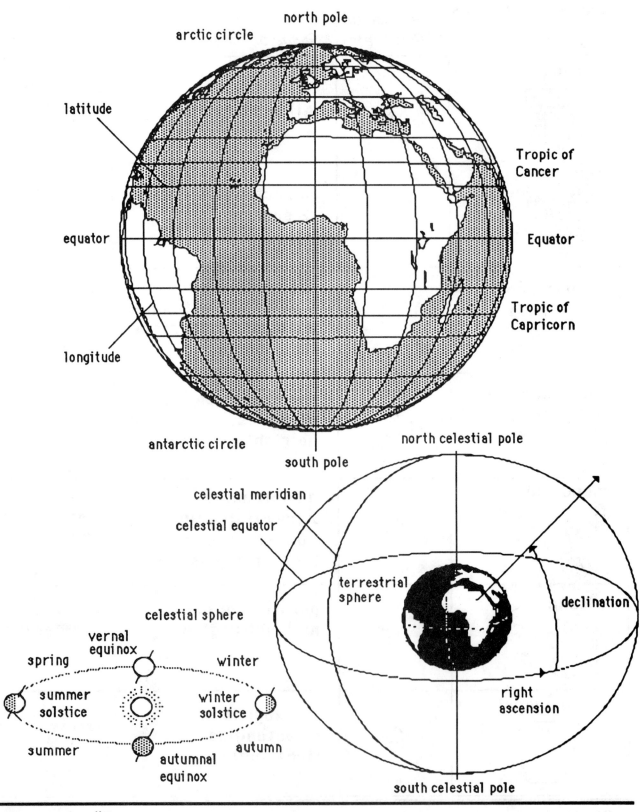

north pole

arctic circle

latitude

Tropic of
Cancer

equator

Equator

Tropic of
Capricorn

longitude

antarctic circle

south pole

north celestial pole

celestial meridian

celestial equator

terrestrial
sphere

declination

celestial sphere

vernal
equinox

spring

winter

summer
solstice

winter
solstice

right
ascension

summer

autumn

autumnal
equinox

south celestial pole

Our Earth #1

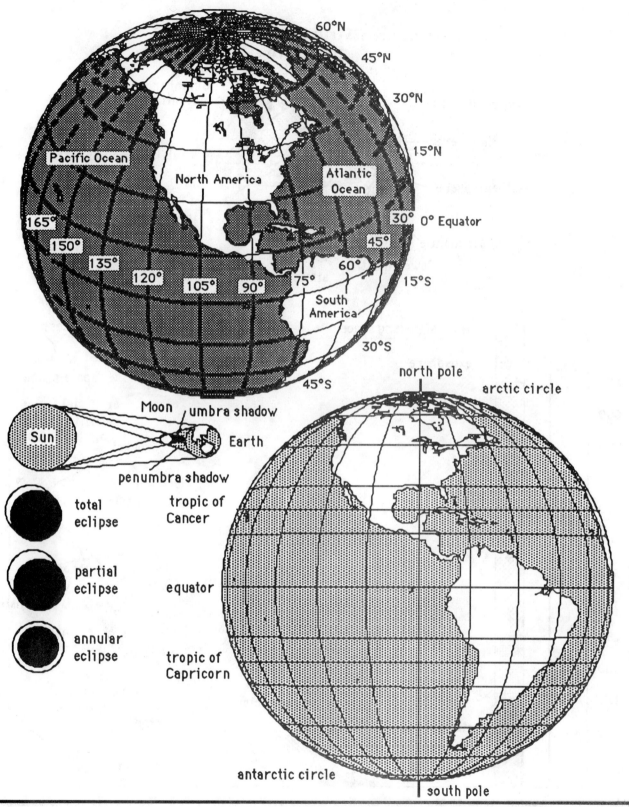

60°N
45°N
30°N
15°N

Pacific Ocean
North America
Atlantic Ocean

165°
150°
135°
120°
105°
90°
75°
60°
45°
30°
0° Equator
15°S
30°S
45°S

South America

Moon   umbra shadow
Sun   Earth
penumbra shadow

total eclipse

partial eclipse

annular eclipse

north pole
arctic circle

tropic of Cancer

equator

tropic of Capricorn

antarctic circle
south pole

Our Earth #2
© 1989 Ventura Educational Systems
All Rights Reserved

Structure of the Earth

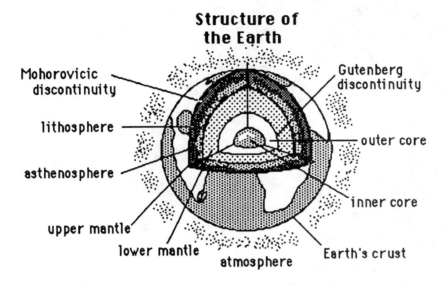

- Mohorovicic discontinuity
- lithosphere
- asthenosphere
- upper mantle
- lower mantle
- atmosphere
- Gutenberg discontinuity
- outer core
- inner core
- Earth's crust

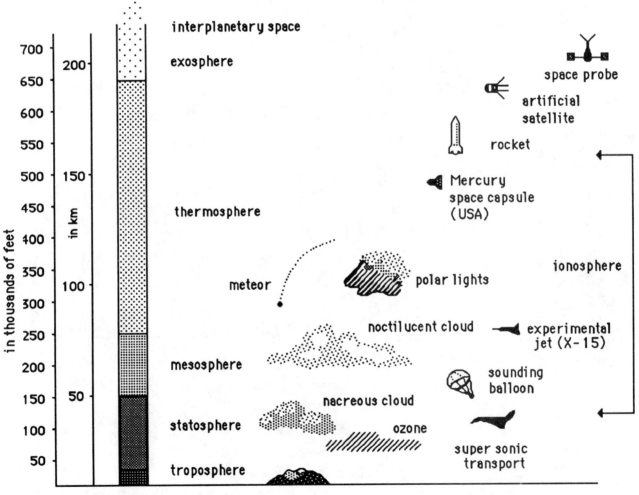

interplanetary space

exosphere

thermosphere

mesosphere

statosphere

troposphere

ionosphere

space probe

artificial satellite

rocket

Mercury space capsule (USA)

polar lights

noctilucent cloud

experimental jet (X-15)

sounding balloon

nacreous cloud

ozone

super sonic transport

meteor

in thousands of feet

in km

700
650
600
550
500
450
400
350
300
250
200
150
100
50

200
150
100
50

Structure of the Earth

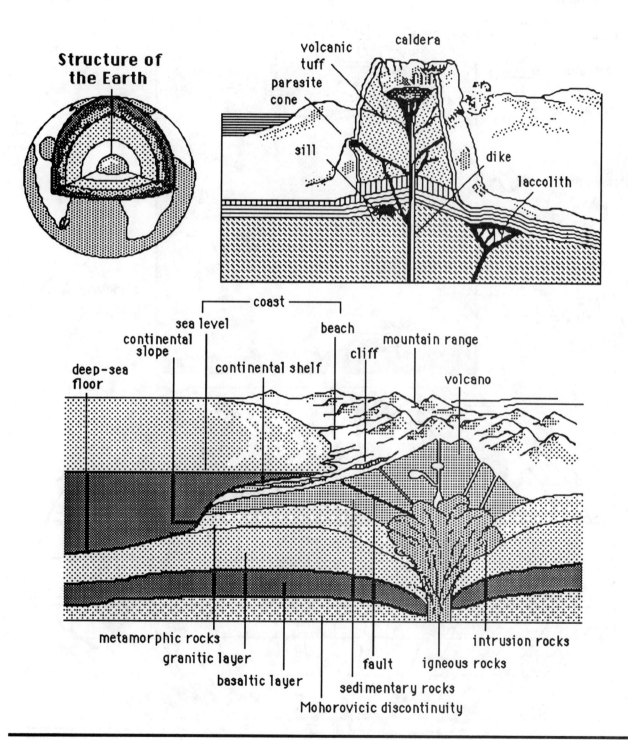

caldera

volcanic tuff

parasite cone

sill

dike

laccolith

coast

sea level

continental slope

beach

mountain range

deep-sea floor

continental shelf

cliff

volcano

metamorphic rocks

granitic layer

basaltic layer

intrusion rocks

fault

igneous rocks

sedimentary rocks

Mohorovicic discontinuity

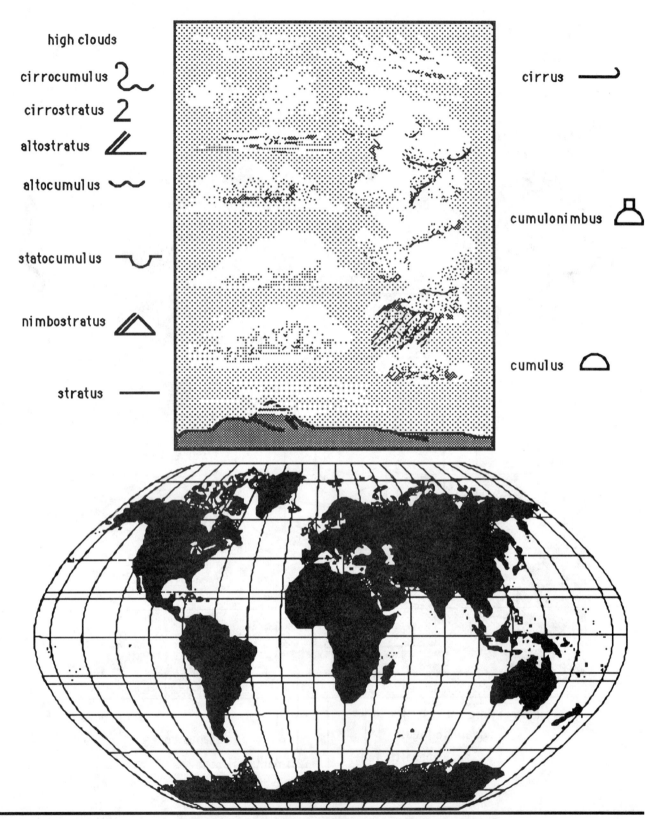

high clouds

cirrocumulus

cirrostratus

altostratus

altocumulus

statocumulus

nimbostratus

stratus

cirrus

cumulonimbus

cumulus

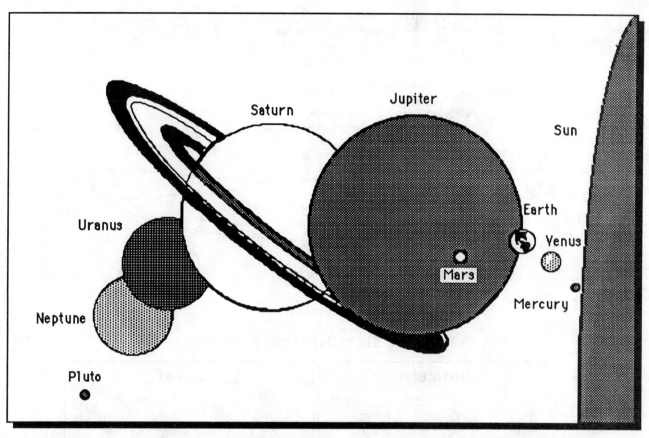

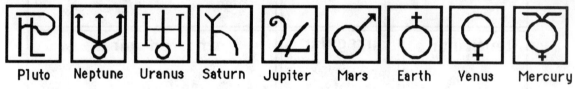

Pluto | Neptune | Uranus | Saturn | Jupiter | Mars | Earth | Venus | Mercury

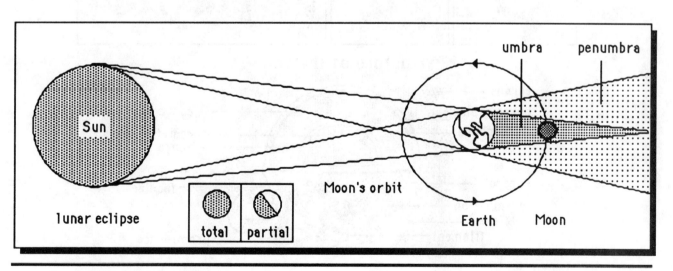

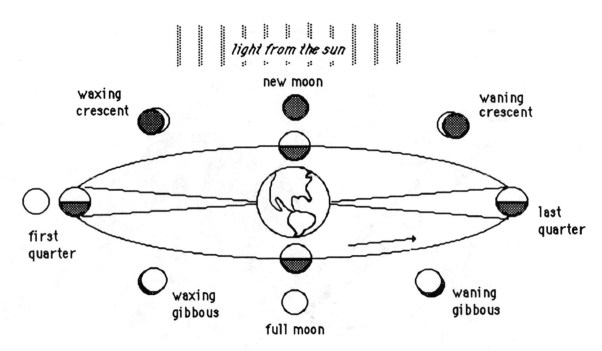

light from the sun

new moon

waxing crescent

waning crescent

first quarter

last quarter

waxing gibbous

waning gibbous

full moon

Hubble's Classification of Galaxies

elliptical

spiral

lenticular

irregular

barred spiral

Structure of the Sun

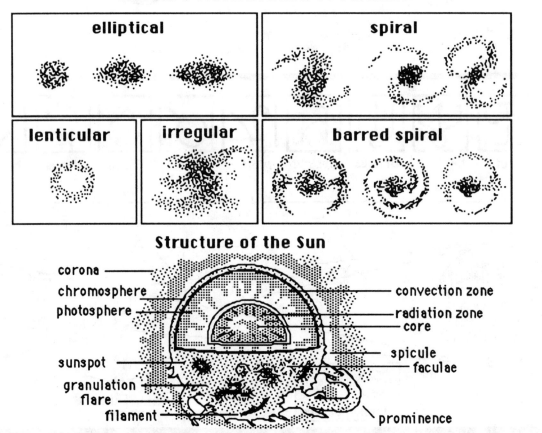

corona

chromosphere

photosphere

convection zone

radiation zone

core

spicule

faculae

sunspot

granulation

flare

filament

prominence

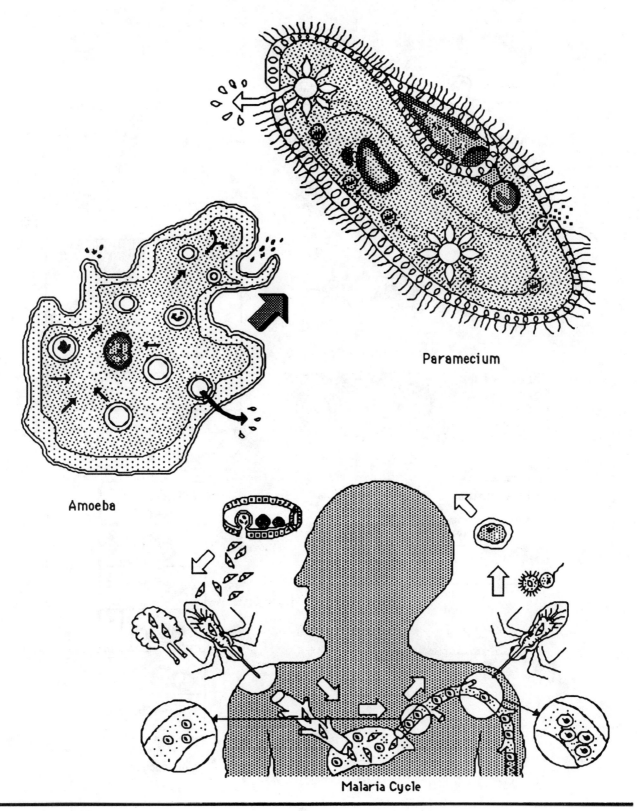

Paramecium

Amoeba

Malaria Cycle

Protozoa #1
© 1989 Ventura Educational Systems

whip-like action of the euglena's flagellum

Euglena
Trichomonas
Volvox

Amoeba
Radiolarian

Paramecium
Tokophyra

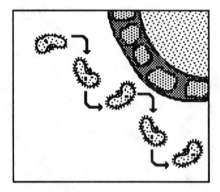

avoidance reaction in paramecium

Plasmodium

mature
form ➚ ←spore

movement of paramecium

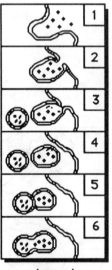

stages in
phagocytosis

Pteranodon

Protoceratops
(herbivore)

Brachiosaurus
(herbivore)

Allosaurus
(carnivore)

Stegosaurus
(plated dinosaur)

Brontosaurus
(herbivore)

Iguanodon
(carnivorous)

Duck-billed Dinosaur
(herbivore)

Dinosaurs

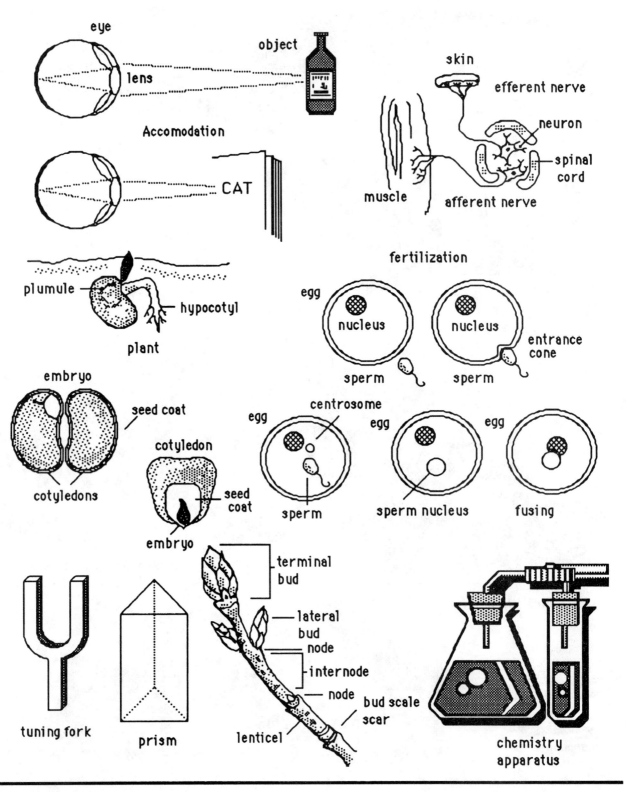

eye

object

lens

Accomodation

CAT

skin

efferent nerve

neuron

spinal cord

muscle

afferent nerve

plumule

hypocotyl

plant

fertilization

egg

nucleus

sperm

egg

nucleus

entrance cone

sperm

embryo

seed coat

cotyledon

cotyledons

seed coat

embryo

centrosome

egg

sperm

egg

sperm nucleus

egg

fusing

terminal bud

lateral bud

node

internode

node

bud scale scar

tuning fork

prism

lenticel

chemistry apparatus

Odds and Ends

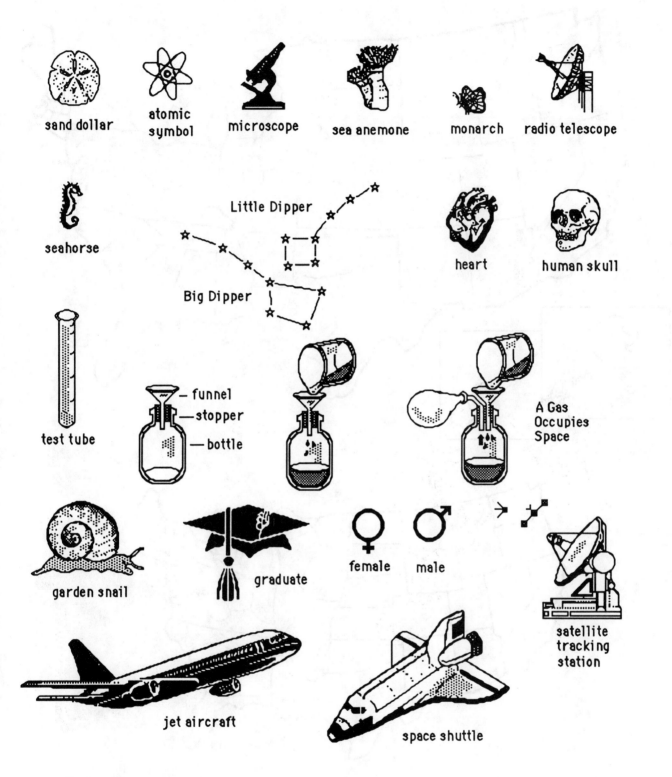

sand dollar

atomic symbol

microscope

sea anemone

monarch

radio telescope

seahorse

Little Dipper

Big Dipper

heart

human skull

test tube

— funnel
— stopper
— bottle

A Gas Occupies Space

garden snail

graduate

female

male

satellite tracking station

jet aircraft

space shuttle

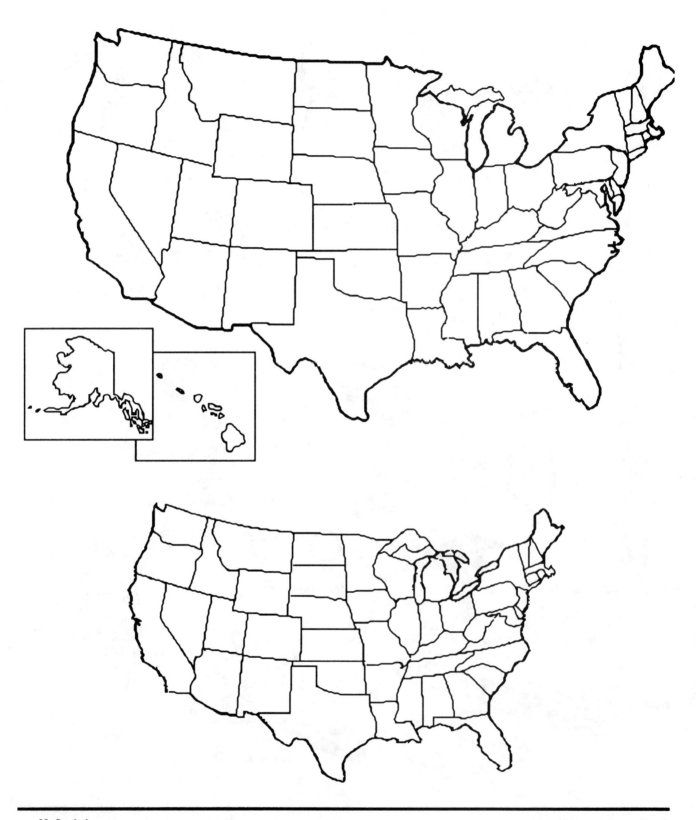

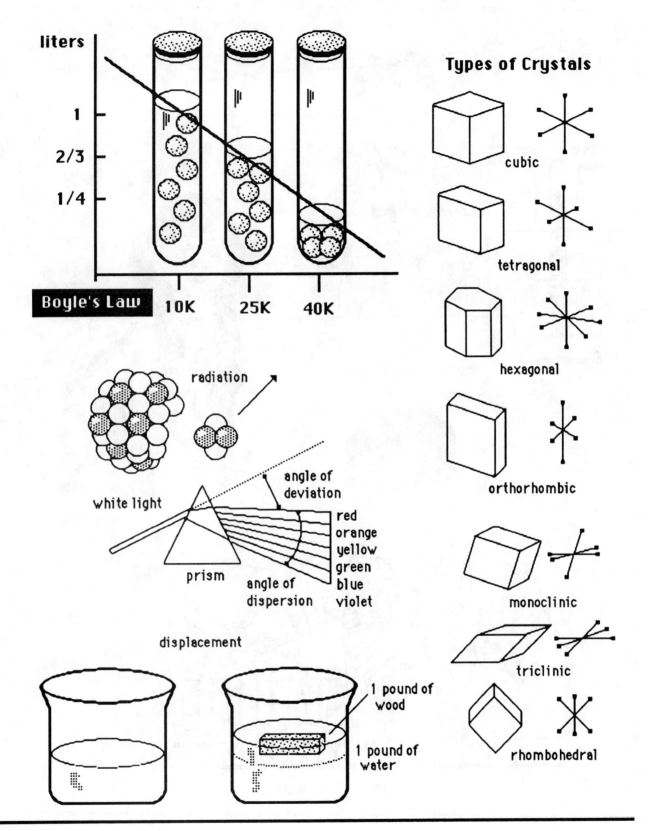

liters

1

2/3

1/4

Boyle's Law   10K   25K   40K

Types of Crystals

cubic

tetragonal

hexagonal

orthorhombic

monoclinic

triclinic

rhombohedral

radiation

white light

prism

angle of deviation

angle of dispersion

red
orange
yellow
green
blue
violet

displacement

1 pound of wood

1 pound of water

sugar
water

water

Boy Observing Osmosis

On to Class

Student Mixing Chemicals

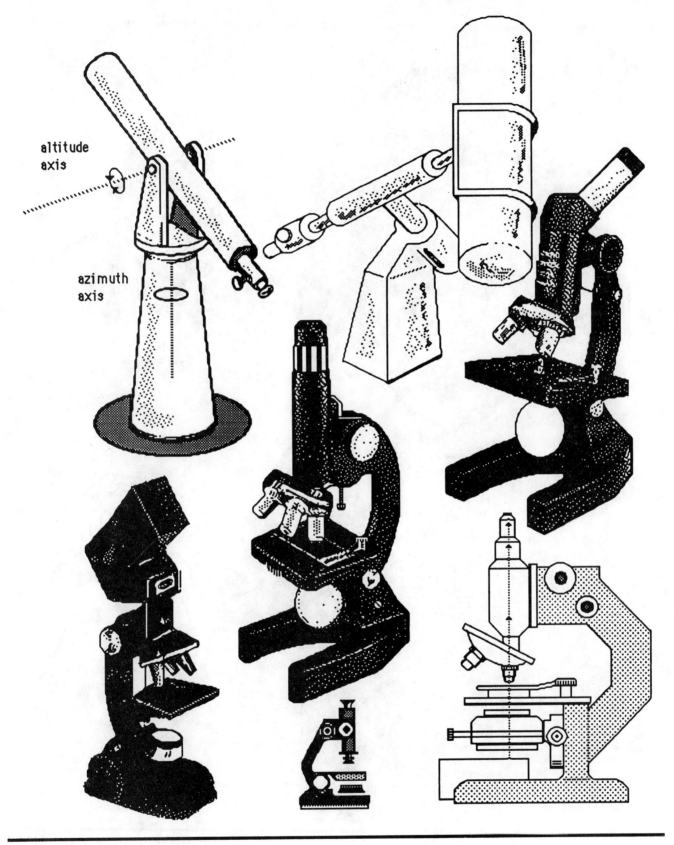

altitude
axis

azimuth
axis

Albert Einstein

Leonardo da Vinci

Benjamin Franklin

Think

Dr. Know

André-Marie Ampère

Charles Darwin

Thomas Edison

Galileo

Robert Fulton

Scientists #2
© 1989 Ventura Educational Systems

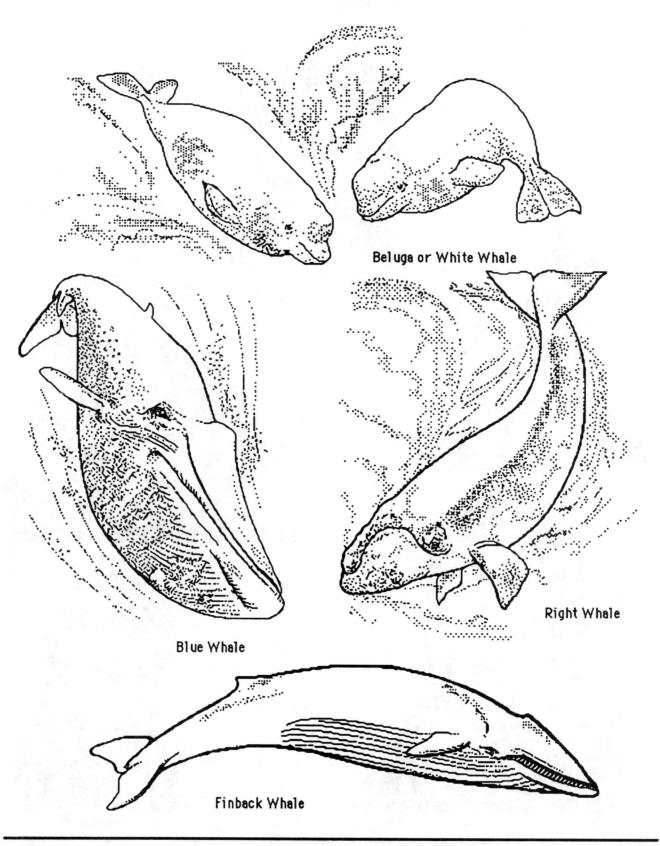

Beluga or White Whale

Blue Whale

Right Whale

Finback Whale

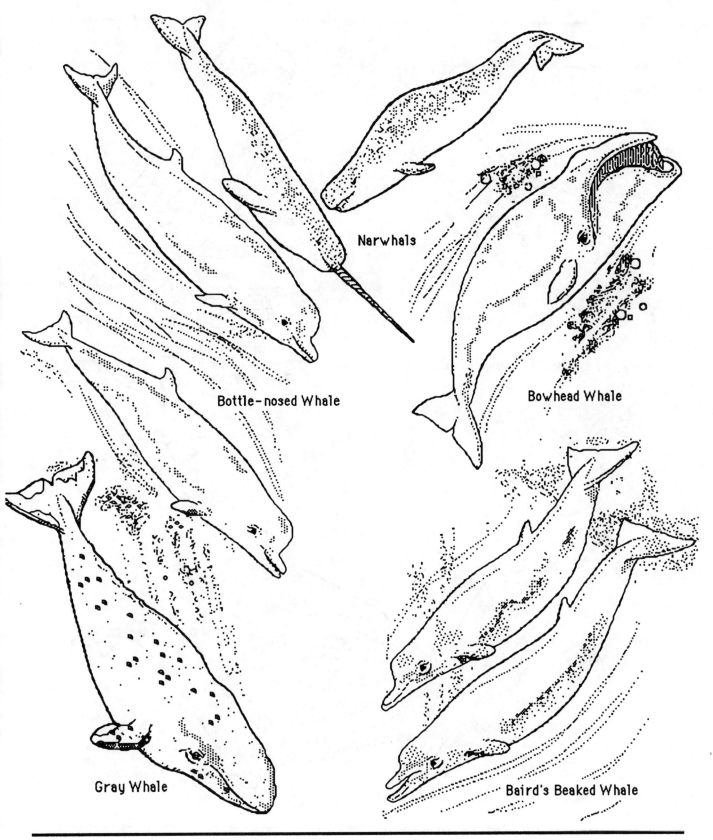

Narwhals

Bottle-nosed Whale

Bowhead Whale

Gray Whale

Baird's Beaked Whale

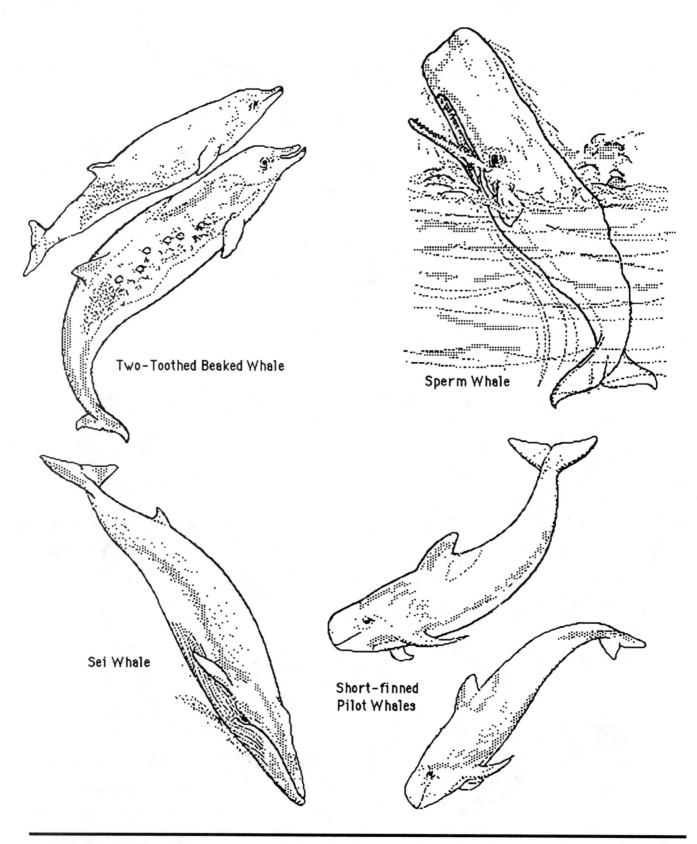

Two-Toothed Beaked Whale

Sperm Whale

Sei Whale

Short-finned
Pilot Whales

Software Order Form

Try these academic learning programs in your classroom!

Order by phone: (800) 336-1022
(805) 499-1407

Ship to:

Name		
School		
School Address		
City	State	ZIP

Bill to:

Name		
School		
School Address		
City	State	ZIP

Check one:

☐ Bill me (school address required). Shipping and handling is extra.

☐ Send programs listed below. Purchase order or payment is enclosed.

If you are not completely satisfied you may return the program in good condition within 30 days for a refund or cancellation of the bill.

Title and Format	Single	Lab-Pack	Quantity	Price	Amount
				Subtotal	
				Tax (in CA)	
				Shipping/ Handling	
				Total	

Write the title and format in the space provided. Please indicate if you would like a singe station version or a lab pack. For lab packs please indicate either 5-pack or 10-pack. A shipping and handling charge will be added to the total, unless order is prepaid. Send your completed order to:

Ventura Educational Systems

✳ 3440 Brokenhill Street ✳ Newbury Park, CA 91320 ✳

Math Manipulatives

Hands-On Math *Volume 1*

Hands-On Math: Volume I simulates the use of six manipulative devices: colored rods, tiles, counters, chip trading, geoboards and tangrams. For each device a program called the playground provides the child with an opportunity to freely explore and discover important mathematical concepts. Using the Playground students can move objects on the screen to experiment with mathematical ideas and fundamental number concepts.

New Hands-On Math *Volume 2*

Hands-On Math: Volume 2 simulates the use of five manipulative devices: two color counters, color tiles, mirrors, attribute blocks and base ten blocks. For each device there are two types of programs. One, called a Playground, is an opportunity for students to investigate a variety of important mathematical ideas. In addition interactive drill and practice type of programs reinforce learning and measure progress.

Teachers can use the Playground to present mathematical ideas in a structured way by following the lessons suggested in the manual. The teacher's guide includes reproducible activity pages designed to lead students through the use of each program and as examples of the engaging learning tasks that students can become involved with using the program.

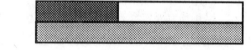

Simulated Color Rods help children learn number concepts, basic operations, fractions and many other math concepts.

Tangrams encourage problem solving and also help children learn about fractions.

Using the geoboard students can learn about geometry and fractions. With chip trading students learn about place value and different bases and with number tiles students learn problem solving by finding the solution to mathematical puzzles.

Hands-On Math programs are available only for Apple // Series Computers. Product includes teacher's guide and reproducible worksheets.

Apple // Versions	**$49.95 each**
Lab Packs	
(5 Program Disks)	**$89.95**
(10 Program Disks)	**$139.95**

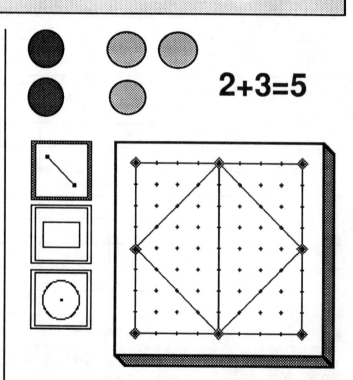

$2+3=5$

Using two color counters students explore basic operations and probability. With the color tiles students can investigate symmetry and using the mirror program students can experiment with reflections. Attribute blocks help to develop logical thinking and base ten blocks build an understanding of place value.

Math Manipulatives

New Hands-On Math   *Volume 3*

Hands-On Math: Volume 3 focuses on the use of six math instructional techniques: a hundreds chart, graphing activities, a number balance, dominoes, aesthenometry and fraction bars. The playground for each technique allows the student to explore and discover math concepts. The exercises are aimed at providing the student with specific activities to practice working with concepts and to help in mastering math objectives.

New Beginning Geometry

Introduce geometry in an exciting way with this activity based learning program. With this program students will explore basic concepts using a geoboard and simulated tangrams. The program provides activities which stress the vocabulary of geometry using a game-like format. Also, the program provides drill and practice in finding the area and perimeter of geometric figures.

By following the examples in the teacher's guide, teachers can lead students to an intuitive understanding of fundamental mathematical concepts. The teacher's guide includes reproducible activity pages which help students use each program and provide classroom teachers with a complete instructional unit.

The hundreds chart activities develop an understanding of numbers and patterns. The activities provide students with an opportunity to practice working with operations and to develop an insight into problem solving.

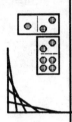

Using the graph center students can quickly and easily make a bar graph of data. Using the balance students create mathematical expressions so that both sides of the balance are equal.

Fraction bars help to develop a conceptual understanding of fractions.

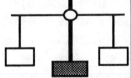

$\frac{1}{4}$ Aesthenometry offers a fun way
$\frac{1}{2}$ to explore geometry and design.

Beginning Geometry encourages exploration and helps to develop an understanding of fundamental geometric concepts using a hands-on interactive approach. The program is supported by reproducible worksheets which help guide student activity while at the computer and provide follow-up learning.

Beginning Geometry is available only for Apple // Series Computers. Product includes teacher's guide and reproducible worksheets.

Apple // Versions	$29.95 each
Lab Packs	
(5 Program Disks)	$69.95
(10 Program Disks)	$119.95

Hands-On Math programs are available only for Apple // Series Computers. Product includes teacher's guide and reproducible worksheets.

Apple // Versions	$49.95 each
Lab Packs	
(5 Program Disks)	$89.95
(10 Program Disks)	$139.95

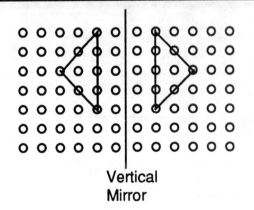

Vertical
Mirror

Mathematics

New Algebra Concepts

Students often feel lost in higher level math classes because they do not understand the terminology and basic concepts of algebra. Algebra Concepts provides a complete introduction to algebra. It uses an interesting game-like format to make algebra exciting.

This program helps first year algebra students learn to solve problems. By focusing on buildng an understanding of the underlying concepts of algebra, the program becomes a tool for real learning.

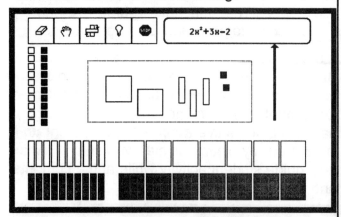

Computer simulated algebra tiles develop a student's understanding of operations with integers, the addition and subtraction of binomials and trinomials, multiplying expressions and factoring. Students move tiles on the screen in order to represent algebraic expressions. The computer automatically evaluates the expression and displays the result on the screen.

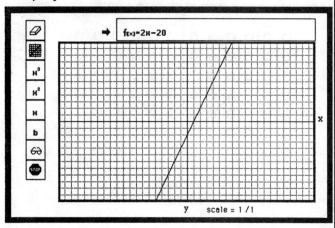

The Function Plot tool allows students to easily define a function and see a graph of the solution set. Students enter a coefficient for each term and then select 'plot'. Instantly the computer graphs the function. The scale of the grid can be changed to 'zoom in' and 'zoom out'.

Using Function Plot students can graph linear and quadratic equations. Since multiple graphs can be drawn on the same grid, the program is useful in illustrating solution sets for simultaneous equations.

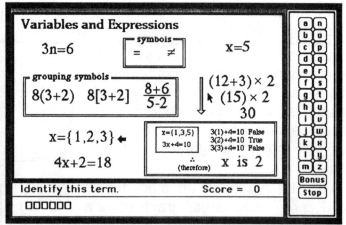

The menu driven format used in the design of Algebra Concepts makes the program easy to use and very flexible. Teachers will find that the program can be adapted and used with students who have very little computer experience. Algebra Concepts creates a learning environment that is both challenging and rewarding for the student

Algebra Concepts is available in Apple //, Macintosh and IBM formats. The product includes a comprehensive teacher's guide and a set of reproducible student worksheets.

All Versions	**$49.95 each**
Lab Packs	
(5 Program Disks)	**$89.95**
(10 Program Disks)	**$139.95**

Mathematics

Geometry Concepts

The features in Geometry Concepts make it a very valuable tool for overcoming the difficulty that many students have in learning geometry. Geometry Concepts helps students learn the terminology of geometry and the informative lessons make it an essential tool for any teacher who uses computers for mathematics instruction.

Geometry concepts is an interactive tutorial and learning game with a database of geometric terms and a multiple choice quiz generating facility. Topics include basic concepts, angles and triangles, circles, area and perimeter, planar figures and solid figures. The program also provides a step-by-step demonstration of five basic constructions. The Macintosh version also has a simulated geoboard and a utility for rotating 3-dimensional shapes.

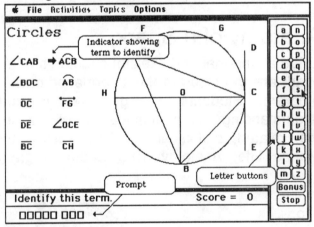

GeoArt

Explore the fascinating relationship between geometry and art with this creative program. Using Geoart students learn about how basic shapes are used in art. The student can create a simple line drawing and then rotate and reflect the line drawing to make an intricate design. Colorful patterns and designs can be automatically repeated by the computer to create tessellations. With the program students can investigate balance, color and other elements of design.

SuperGraph

Few function plotting programs offer the number of features found in SuperGraph. First year algebra students can use it to graph linear and quadratic equations. More advanced students can use it to learn trigonometry and calculus. SuperGraph can plot any user defined function. Built-in functions include SIN, COS, TAN, and SQR. Many derived functions are also included, for example, inverse cosine, inverse hyperbolic cosine, inverse cotangent, cosecant, log, and hyperbolic tangent. Product includes a program disk, a data disk with many examples and a teacher's guide with reproducible masters to direct student's use of the program.

Coordinate Geometry

Coordinate Geometry features tutorials introducing the Cartesian Plane. In addition to self-paced lessons, students can define equations for the computer to graph or take a quiz with randomly generated problems.

Topics include (x,y) coordinates, defining a locus, and defining lines (y=x, y=x+b, y=mx and y=mx+b). The program includes a complete teacher's guide and supplemental worksheets which can be reproduced for classroom use.

All programs are available as Lab Packs and include a teacher's guide and reproducible student worksheets.

		Lab Pack (5)
Geometry Concepts		
Apple //, Macintosh or IBM Versions	$49.95	
Lab Packs (5)	$89.95	
Lab Packs (10)	$139.95	
GeoArt (Apple //)	$49.95	$89.95
SuperGraph (Apple //)	$59.95	$99.95
Coordinate Geometry	$49.95	$89.95
(Apple // or Macintosh)		

Marine Life Series

Marine Invertebrates

Explore the wonders of sea life with this fascinating program. Marine Invertebrates presents information on the sponge, sea anemone, clam and starfish. Students learn about how these simple animals live.

Anatomy of a Fish

Basic anatomical structures and functions are the subject of this interesting program which covers external, internal and skeletal structures of bony fish. Students learn about how various parts work together to support life.

In each Marine Life Series program lessons present basic information on each topic. The lessons are illustrated by a detailed graphic. A probe allows students to move an indicator to parts of the animal and retrieve detailed information about the biological function of a particular structure.

Word games are used to reinforce science vocabulary. These games are designed to help students learn to identify anatomical structures and associated biological functions, and to learn the special vocabulary that pertains to marine biology. Students will also learn to spell many biological terms. Each program also contains a series of quizzes. The quizzes generate multiple choice and true false questions based on the information that has been presented in the lessons and probes. All the programs include a teacher's guide with worksheets that are correlated with the computer-based activities.

Sea Lamprey

Learn about the strange and fascinating life cycle and anatomy of the sea lamprey with this program. The Sea Lamprey will stimulate student's interest in marine biology and works in conjunction with the other three programs in providing a complete unit on comparative anatomy.

Anatomy of a Shark

External, internal and skeletal structures of the shark are the focus of this information-packed program. Students will gain an in-depth understanding of anatomical structures and the related biological functions using the Marine Life: Anatomy of a Shark program.

Marine Life Series programs are available for Apple //, Macintosh and IBM Computers. Product includes teacher's guide and reproducible worksheets.

All Versions	**$49.95 each**
Lab Packs	
(5 Program Disks)	**$89.95**
(10 Program Disks)	**$139.95**
All Four Programs	**$169.95**

All About Science Series

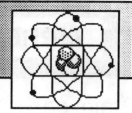

All About the Solar System

The sun, the earth and moon, the inner planets and the outer planets are the topics covered in this intriguing and informative program. It is an excellent resource for research projects using the computer to find information. Correlated worksheets provide follow-up activities.

All About Matter

Atoms, molecules and states of matter are the subject of this learning system. The lessons introduce atomic structure and molecules. Students learn about solids, liquids and gases, and the processes used to change a substance from one state of matter to another.

In each All About Science program lessons present basic information on the particular topic. The lessons are illustrated using high resolution color graphics. Students can learn the vocabulary associated with each topic by moving an indicator to a part of the graphic and retrieving detailed information about the science term represented by the diagram.

Three word games are included with each program. These games are designed to help students learn the key science terms and associated concepts. The focus is to learn the science vocabulary that pertains to elementary science curriculum. Students will enjoy learning to spell and define the terms. Each program also contains a series of quizzes. The quizzes generate multiple choice and true false questions based on the information that has been presented in the lessons and probes. All the programs include a teacher's guide with worksheets that are correlated to the computer-based activities.

All About Simple Machines

This informative program focuses on the history and function of the gear, inclined plane, pulley, screw and wheel. Students learn about how each simple machine helps to reduce the effort needed to do work.

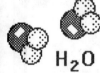

H_2O The teacher's guide includes suggested experiments that reinforce concepts learned while using the software.

The menu system provides flexibility and allows the teacher to direct the student's learning.

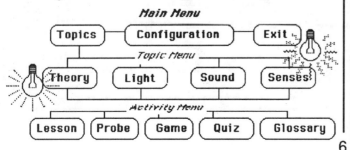

All About Light and Sound

Light as a form of radiant energy, the particle theory and the wave theory of light, reflection and refraction, the characteristics of sound, voices, hearing and communication are all topics covered in this informative program.

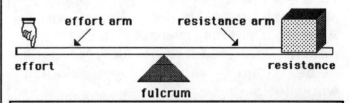

All About Science Series programs are available only for Apple // Series Computers. Product includes teacher's guide and reproducible worksheets.

Apple // Version	**$49.95 each**
Lab Packs	
(5 Program Disks)	**$89.95**
(10 Program Disks)	**$139.95**
All Four Programs	**$169.95**

6

General Biology

Protozoa

Students can use Protozoa to explore the fascinating life process of single-celled organisms. The program introduces students to the structures and biological functions of four important, representative microorganisms: Euglena, Amoeba, Paramecium and Plasmodium.

Activities include an identification game, a multiple choice quiz and a utility for retrieving detailed information from a database where the records are linked to the computer graphic.

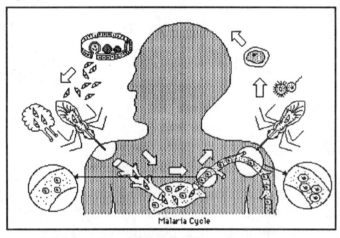

Malaria Cycle

Protozoa is available in Apple //, Macintosh and IBM formats. Plant & Animals Cells is available in Apple // format. Both products include a teacher's guide and reproducible student worksheets.

Protozoa
Apple // , Macintosh	
or IBM Versions	$49.95
Lab Pack (5)	$89.95
Lab Pack (10)	$139.95

Plant and Animal Cells	$49.95
Lab Pack (5)	$89.95

Plant and Animal Cells

This program explores the mysteries of the cell. Plant and Animals Cells presents information on the general structure of plant cells, photosynthesis, the general structure of animal cells and mitosis.

An illustrated lesson presents informational text. Color graphics are used to show details of cell biology.

The program also includes a section called 'the probe' where students can move an indicator to an illustrated part of the cell and review information on how the part functions.

Several motivating, vocabulary-building games are included in this program. The games are useful for reinforcement and involve the identification of parts, spelling science terms and recognizing the definition of science terms.

Multiple choice and true/false quizzes are used for measuring student progress in comprehending the information presented using the tutorials and probes.

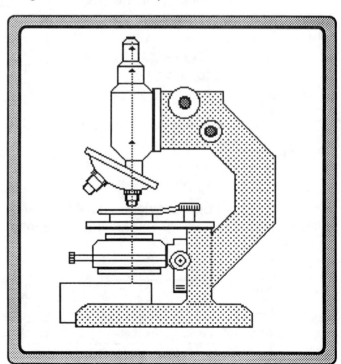

General Biology

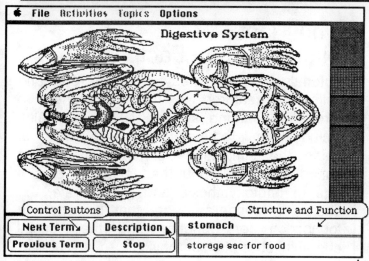

VisiFrog

Learning the anatomy of a frog can be fun with this program. Detailed graphics make using the program useful for both individual students and for classroom or group demonstrations.

VisiFrog introduces the frog's anatomical structures and biological functions. Computer graphics are used to represent the skeletal system, nervous system, cardiovascular system, reproductive system and the musculature. Textual information is linked to parts of the graphic. The activities include playing an identification game, using the database to find information and answering a multiple choice quiz.

The Earthworm

The study of invertebrate anatomy is an essential part of the biology curriculum. Teachers and students will find the program a perfect complement to dissection units. The Worm introduces the anatomical structures and functions of the earthworm. Topics include digestion, sensation, control and reproduction. A cross-sectional view is provided. Activities include identifying parts of the worm represented by computer graphics, referencing the database to find information and answering questions in a multiple choice quiz.

Senses

Explore the fascinating workings and intricate parts of the human sense organs. Using this program students gain an in-depth understanding of the mysteries of human perception. The program includes a learning game, a database and a multiple choice quiz designed to make learning fun. Detailed drawings of the five sense organs help students learn to recognize the names of the intricate structures and their functions.

Five anatomical drawings are used to illustrate the parts of the sense organs.

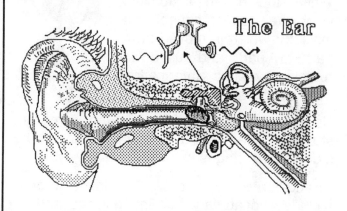

Visifrog, The Earthworm and Senses are available in Apple //, Macintosh and IBM formats and include a teacher's guide and reproducible student worksheets.

Apple //, Macintosh or IBM Versions	**$49.95**
Lab Packs	
5 Program Disks	**$89.95**
10 Program Disks	**$139.95**

General Science: Plants and Insects

The Insect World

Using the tutorials in The Insect World students learn that there are harmful and beneficial types of insects. The lessons cover the insect's basic body parts: exoskeleton, head, thorax, abdomen and internal systems. Student will find the information on how insects survive fascinating.

This three-disk, information-packed learning system includes a special program called the X-ray Machine where students can view the internal structures, the respiratory system or the nervous system of a grasshopper.

While studying an anatomical view, the student controls an indicator which is moved from part to part and used to retrieve detailed information from a database.

Using another section of the program students learn about metamorphosis by studying the stages in a butterfly's life cycle.

In addition to the tutorials The Insect World includes vocabulary building quizzes and a complete, computer-based glossary of terms. Teachers will find the reproducible activity pages a valuable source of lesson ideas that provide follow-up and reinforcement for the program.

> **The Insect World and The Plant: Nature's Food Factory are both three-disk learning systems.**

Apple // Versions	$69.95
Lab Packs	$189.95

All programs include a teacher's guide and reproducible activity pages.

The Plant: Nature's Food Factory

Tutorials on flowers, leaves, stems, roots and cells are featured in this comprehensive three-disk learning system. The Plant also includes simulated experiments with plants. In doing the simulations students manipulate variables to learn about the factors that control rate of photosynthesis and growth rate, the basis for Mendel's theory that became the foundation for genetics and the special characteristics of chlorophyll.

In addition to tutorials and simulated experiments The Plant also includes a variety of word games that help build science vocabulary. Motivating word games challenge students to match terms and definitions and correctly spell the words that have been encountered in the self-paced tutorials.

Also included is a computer-based glossary which students can use to find a definition for the science words they encounter in the program.

High-resolution color graphics are used extensively in this program to add interest and stimulate learning. Diagrams are used to illustrate the parts of a plant, plant cells and in the simulated experiments.

The Plant: Nature's Food Factory is an excellent tool for teachers who are using computers to enhance their science curriculum.

This program, when used with the reproducible activity pages, is a complete unit on plants which is appropriate for upper elementary and intermediate level students.

Chemistry and Computers

New Version Chemaid

Chemaid makes learning the periodic table fun. The program is an information resource that presents the elements according to their symbol, classification and position.

Students will enjoy the challenging identification game where the objective is to correctly recognize and spell the name of an element based on its position in the chart.

Chemaid also includes a database which allows students to access information on each element. The database includes information on the atomic number, atomic weight, electron configuration and specific gravity. Each element is classified in a group, for example, alkali metals. Students will read about the uses for an element and some of its special properties.

Chemaid is a great resource for the science classroom and can be used by students for research projects. In completing the activities students will use the computer as a tool for finding and organizing information. Teachers will find that the program is adaptable and can be used to develop higher level thinking skills.

Computer Concepts

Computer Concepts is perfect for introductory computer literacy courses. The program provides an excellent overview of computer fundamentals and the topics covered have become an essential part of the curriculum for an information age. The easy-to-use menus and game-like format make Computer Concepts fun for students who are new to computers.

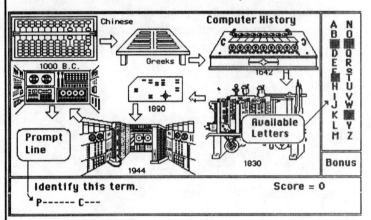

Computer Concepts provides a survey of important topics in computer literacy. The program uses a game-like format to teach terms and key concepts relevant to Computer History, How a Computer System Works, BASIC Statements, Understanding Computers, Flowcharts, Computer Uses, Computer Components and Peripherals.

Computer Concepts is available for Apple // series, Macintosh and IBM computers. Chemaid is available for Apple // series and Macintosh computers. Product includes a teacher's guide and reproducible activity pages.

Apple //, Macintosh and IBM Versions	**$49.95**
Lab Pack (5 disks)	**$89.95**
Lab Pack (10 disks)	**$139.95**

New Version

Speech Synthesis in Macintosh Version

States: Geography Study Unit

The States Geography Study Unit presents the states and capitals of the U.S. as parts of nine geographical regions. Identification games and a powerful database make learning interesting and rewarding for students.

Teachers will love the motivation that develops when students play the identification games. During the games students are given a location on a map showing a region of the U.S. and are challenged to spell the names of the states or capitals.

The Apple // version of States features detailed colorful maps and the Macintosh version features the use of synthesized speech.

The program randomly generates multiple choice quizzes where the object is to match a state with its capital. During the quiz a score is maintained and a performance report is provided at the end of the quiz.

States is available for Apple // series or Macintosh computers. Product includes a teacher's guide and reproducible activity pages to duplicate for students.

Apple // or Macintosh Version	**$49.95**
Lab Pack (5)	**$89.95**
Lab Pack (10)	**$139.95**

The powerful database gives students instant access to hundreds of interesting facts. Using the database students can make a query to find information. For example, the student can direct the computer to list all states with a population greater than 1 million. Once the list has been retrieved the student might look at the location or major industry of these states.

While using the database to explore the information about the 50 states, the student can instantly call up a map to see the location of the state.

Because the States Geography Study Unit presents each state as part of a geographic region, students learn that the states in each region have similar characteristics.

Database Facts Include:

State	Population
Capital	Area
Main Industry	Electoral Votes
State Bird	U.S. Representatives
State Flower	Admission Date

Statistical Functions:

Total	Minimum
Average	Maximum

Sorting Functions:

Ascending Arrangement
Descending Arrangement

A new statistics feature has been added so that students can find the sum, average, highest or lowest value for any field. Students can answer many types of questions using this feature. For example, the student could find the average population of all states where corn is a major industry.

Clip-Art for Teachers

Clip-Art for Science Teachers

This useful clip-art collection provides science teachers with a wide variety of detailed diagrams that can be added to tests, reports, overhead transparencies and worksheets. Paste some of these diagrams into teacher prepared materials and watch students' interest increase.

Clip-Art for Math Teachers

Make math tests come alive with this exciting new collection of clip-art images. Clip-art for Math Teachers contains a wide variety of images and can be used by both elementary and secondary level teachers.

Each graphic is stored as a standard bit-map image. The Clip-Art for Teachers diagrams are in MacPaint format and can be used as is or can be edited with most paint programs such as MacPaint, FullPaint, or SuperPaint. Color can be added with PixelPaint. Clip-Art for Teachers can also be used with many test generators.

Make your teacher prepared educational materials more interesting by using Clip-Art for Teachers. Worksheets with detailed drawings can be easily created. These well-rounded collections of diagrams would be useful to most teachers.

**The categories included
in Clip-Art for Science Teachers:**

Biology
Earth and Space
Microorganisms

Science Lab
Frogs, Whales, Clams
and Worms
and More...

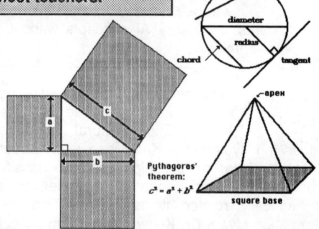

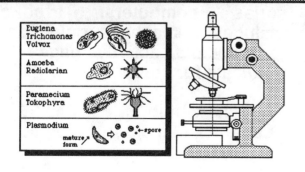

The categories included in Clip-Art for Math Teachers:

Geometry   Mathematicians
Algebra   Theorems
Fractions   Solids
                History of Mathematics

Artificial Intelligence

Dr. Know:
Experiments in Artificial Intelligence

Dr. Know is an experience with the future of educational computing that shows how a computer can be used to simulate thinking. Artificial Intelligence (AI) is the next step in computer learning and Dr. Know is the perfect tool for exploring the potential for AI in the classroom. Dr. Know will help students keep up with the latest developments in computer technology.

☐ Activities for exploring the fundamental concepts of Artificial Intelligence.

☐ Amazing hands-on activities supported by ready-to use classroom materials.

☐ An easy-to-use menu that allows students to explore AI concepts without programming.

Logic: Dr. Know performs logical reasoning based on the information entered by the student. Using a simple natural language processing system Dr. Know can learn about the hierarchical relationships used to classify plants, animals, rocks, foods or any other set of hierarchically related items. Based on the information given, Dr. Know can perform logical reasoning to derive a conclusion and can even explain the reasoning used to get to a conclusion.

Expert Systems: Students can teach Dr. Know to be an expert and will be fascinated as they watch Dr. Know learn and master a subject. For example, students can teach Dr. Know how to identify a certain type of rock or mineral, how to determine the presence of a certain element in a compound or how to recognize a certain type of animal or plant. Dr. Know can learn anything that can be determined by a series of tests.

Challenging Games: Dr. Know also plays several challenging logic games and can be used to teach problem solving. For example, to solve one of the puzzles the students need to formulate a hypothesis, test the hypothesis and deduce the rules from the feedback given by the computer.

Dr. Know makes it easy for teachers to integrate AI into the standard curriculum. Dr. Know will become a guide to your students as they explore the world of artificial intelligence. Once you invite Dr. Know into your classroom, your understanding of what you can do with computers will change and new possibilities will be open to you and your students.

The teacher's guide and reproducible activity pages help teachers plan lessons that incorporate the use of AI. Suggested activities relate to the math and science curriculum. Dr. Know will easily become an exciting part of your computer literacy curriculum.

Because the acitivities that students engage in while using Dr. Know involve higher-order thinking skills it is appropriate for Gifted and Talented programs.

Dr. Know is available for Apple // series computers. Product includes a teacher's guide and reproducible activity pages to duplicate for students.

Apple // Version	**$49.95**
Lab Pack (5 disks)	**$89.95**

13

Music

Music Concepts

This unique, easy-to-use program introduces basic concepts of music pertaining to music theory, music history and the science of sound.

Music Concepts is a two disk learning system. The first disk contains the music terminology study unit, a data retrieval utility and a program that generates multiple choice quizzes based on the terms and concepts learned while using the program.

Topics covered on the first disk include Music Symbols and Notation, Types of Instruments, Composers, the Orchestra and the Physics and Physiology of Sound.

Students learn about these subjects while interacting with the computer in a game-like activity. High-resolution color graphics are used to illustrate the terms and key concepts.

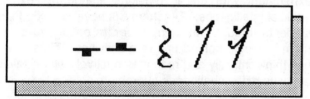

The reproducible activity pages supplied with the program guide students in researching the data to find answers to questions. Using the computer and the worksheets students develop reading skills while learning about music.

The second disk in this learning system contains programs where students can experiment with music.

The program titled Melody Match challenges the student to listen to a simple melody and then match what was heard to what is represented on the screen in musical notation.

Another program called Rhythm Match plays a pattern of notes and then challenges the student to select the correct musical notation for what was heard.

Another program titled The Composer allows students to enter simple melodies by placing notes on a staff that is represented on the screen and then to play back the melodies.

Music Concepts will take advantage of Mockingboard Compatible Synthesizer Cards if present in the system.

What the Reviewers Say...

Hands-On Math

"Ventura Educational Systems is bridging the gap between the use of manipulatives in the math classroom and the representation of manipulatives in computer software."

**--The Computing Teacher
October 1988**

"We understand that the mathematics learning continuum begins with concrete, moves through pictorial, then advances to abstract. (Hands-On Math) fits into this continuum beautifully. This excellent program simulates the use of manipulatives. In this way it actually forms a bridge bewtween concrete and pictorial and moves into abstract at the program's higher levels. "

**--Teaching K-8
January 1989**

"One particularly strong aspect of this program is the collection of reproducible student Activity Pages found in the binder. These pages include a varied range of challenges for elementary and middle school students. --- The purchase of this program is highly recommended as reinforcement to the learning of basic mathematics concepts with manipulative materials. Not only is the program pedagogically sound, but it is a lot of fun to use."

**--Journal of Computers in
Mathematics and Science
Teaching (Spring 1989)**

Coordinate Geometry

"A wonderful coordination between graphics and instruction. Clean, well-defined screens, good lessons and quizzes. Beautiful program."

**-- UCCS Colorado Springs
(August 1988)**

States

"The program can be used to review states and capitals and to learn more facts about and locations of the states. Students can work individually or compete in small groups. The graphics are very well done. Students can operate easily as it is menu-driven."

**--Florida Department of
Education, microSIFT**

GeoArt

"Can be used at several grade levels in reviewing the characteristics of common geometric figures and calculating the perimeter and area."

**--Region X ESC,
Richardson, Texas microSIFT**

VisiFrog

"VisiFrog is an exceptionally easy program to use and requires very little time to learn. ...The real strength of the program lies in its flexibility. The information in the program is useful for a range of learning situations."

**--Journal of Computers in
Mathematics and Science
Teaching (Spring 1985)**

Dr. Know

"Dr. Know is not a flashy program, but it is a relatively good and inexpensive attempt to allow students to experiment with the increasingly important field of artificial intelligence. Teachers will have to guide their students through the many program options to show them the logic behind program activities. Those who can think critically and reason deductively will certainly enjoy its many challenges at problem solving."

**-- Educational Technology
(January 1988)**

You be the judge!

Order a 30-day preview copy of any program.